This Twirlywoos
annual belongs to:

....

Twirlywoos and all related titles, logos and characters are trademarks of DHX Worldwide Ltd.
© 2016 Ragdoll Productions Ltd/DHX Worldwide Ltd
All rights reserved
www.Twirlywoos.com

Some images © Shutterstock

Written by Lydia Barram and Stella Gurney

Cover designed by Anna Lubecka

Interior designed by Gary Knight, Anna Lubecka and Wayne Redwood

Production by Amy Knight

First published in the UK in 2016 by HarperCollins Children's Books.
HarperCollins Children's Books is a division of HarperCollins Publishers Ltd,
1 London Bridge Street, London, SE1 9GF

1 3 5 7 9 10 8 6 4 2

ISBN: 978-0-00-816958-9

www.harpercollins.co.uk

All rights reserved

Printed and bound in Italy

Ragdoll

media®
dhx

HarperCollins *Children's Books*

FSC
www.fsc.org

MIX
Paper from
responsible sources
FSC™ C007454

FSC™ is a non-profit international organisation established to promote
the responsible management of the world's forests. Products carrying the
FSC label are independently certified to assure consumers that they come
from forests that are managed to meet the social, economic and
ecological needs of present and future generations,
and other controlled sources.

Find out more about HarperCollins and the environment at
www.harpercollins.co.uk/green

twirly wOOs™

Annual 2017

Contents

Quack! Quack! Quack!

Quacky Birds fly over the sea.
Bring the Boat close home to me.

It's **The Big Red Boat!**

Great BigHoo

Here are the **Twirlywoos!**

and **Toodloo**

Chickedy and Chick!

And Peekaboo!

Hello **Twirlywoos!** Let's go and learn something new.

Today the **Twirlywoos** are learning something new. All about... **Smaller!**

Look at **Toodloo**. She is SMALLER than Great BigHoo.

Now look at **Chickedy** and **Chick**. They are SMALLER than Toodloo!

And **Peekaboo** is the SMALLEST of them all!

Look at all the **characters** on the page.
Point to the **SMALLER** one in each pair.

Back to The
Big Red Boat,
Twirlywoos!

11

Smaller!

Bang!

Bang!

What's that?

It's somebody at the door.

The Twirlywoos fall over in surprise.

Who is it?

It's **The Very Important Lady!** She has come to visit the Twirlywoos on The Big Red Boat. She sings a lovely hello song.

Oh no!

The Very Important Lady sang so loudly, she fell apart.

Don't worry, Very Important Lady, the Twirlywoos will put you back together again.

Oh dear – that's not right!

The Twirlywoos try again.

Oh no! Now, she's even SMALLER...

Try again, Twirlywoos!

Now The Very Important Lady is **much** too SMALL!

The Twirlywoos try one last time.

Well done, Twirlywoos!

The Very Important Lady is happy. Now she can sing again.

La-la-laaaa!

It's The Very Important Lady!

Colour in The Very Important Lady's dress. Start at the bottom with the big piece and go up. What colour is left for her arms?

1 Pink
2 Red
3 Orange
4 Yellow
5 Blue

The Stop-Go Car has brought lots of shapes.

Find all the SMALLER shapes and colour them blue.

17

Some people are BIGGER. Some people are SMALLER.

Who lives in your house? Is anyone SMALLER than you?

Draw them here!

Can you make yourself even SMALLER, just like Peekaboo?

Sit on the floor... Now you are SMALLER.

Curl up in a ball... Now you are even SMALLER!

Are YOU SMALLER than anyone in your house? Who?

Draw them here!

Who is the SMALLEST in your house?

Is it you?

Draw them here!

Today the **Twirlywoos** are learning something new. All about... **Full!**

This bowl is **FULL** of... fruit.

This teapot is **FULL** of... tea.

This pot is **FULL** of... flowers.

This box is **FULL** of... toys.

Can you think of anything else that can be **FULL**?

Full!

It's the **Twirlywoos!**

They are all on
The Big Red Boat.

Great BigHoo

and **Toodloo,**

Chickedy,

Chick!

And Peekaboo!

Great BigHoo is fetching the Fruit Tea today. Here's the **Fruit Tea Machine.**

And here's the teapot. The teapot is empty. But Great BigHoo will make it... FULL!

Great BigHoo presses the pedal. The Fruit Tea comes up and up and up.

The Fruit Tea Machine is getting FULL.

It's Watermelon Tea today!

Well done Great BigHoo! The Teapot is FULL.

Great BigHoo pours Fruit Tea into Chickedy and Chick's bowls. FULL!

He pours Fruit Tea into Toodloo's bowl. FULL!

He fills his bowl last. All the Twirlywoos' bowls are now FULL!

The Twirlywoos are very thirsty.
They **drink** and **drink** and **drink**.

Glug

Glug

Glug!

Now the teapot and their bowls are empty.

Oh dear! The **Twirlywoos** are FULL!

Chickedy!

Chick!

Toodloo!

Hoo!

No more Fruit Tea for you today, Twirlywoos!

The Twirlywoos want to drink Fruit Tea – but there is no Fruit Tea in the teapot! Colour it in so it is FULL!

Look at all these things! Some of them are **FULL**, and some of them are empty.
Circle all the ones that are **FULL**.

Toodloo wants to get back to the rest of the Twirlywoos and have a picnic. Find her a path that takes her past only **FULL** things on the way.

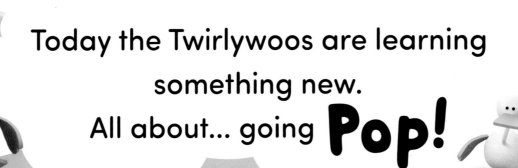

Today the Twirlywoos are learning something new.
All about... going **Pop!**

Bubbles can go POP.

Balls can go POP.

Balloons can go POP.

The **Twirlywoos** love to make things go POP.

Touch all the things on the page that can go POP. How many are there?

Pop!

Hello Twirlywoos!
Great BigHoo, Toodloo, Chickedy and Chick are all having Fruit Tea on The Big Red Boat.

What's that?
Someone is blowing bubbles.

Shhh...

How many bubbles are there? Can you count them?

It's Peekaboo!

Pop!

The bubbles float higher and higher, until...

Pop! Pop! The bubbles burst. POP!

Pop!

Pop!

The **Twirlywoos** are so surprised, they throw their Fruit Tea up into the air, until...

Splosh!

It falls back into their bowls again. That was lucky, Twirlywoos!

Here is **Peekaboo.** He's blowing bubbles again...
Look at this very big bubble!

The very big bubble
floats over to the
table, and on to
the Twirlywoos!

They float
up and ^up^ and ^up^ until...

They are in the very big
bubble! What will you do,
Twirlywoos?

Pop!

The very **big** bubble bursts!

The **Twirlywoos**
all float back down.
But where is
their Fruit Tea?

They all look up and hold out their bowls. They wait and wait, until...

Splosh!

It lands back in their bowls.

Chick!

Chickedy!

Toodloo!

Hoo!

Phew. No more bubbles today please, Peekaboo!

Look at all the lovely bubbles! Some of them have gone POP – colour in the bubbles that are left.

Draw some more bubbles for them to POP!

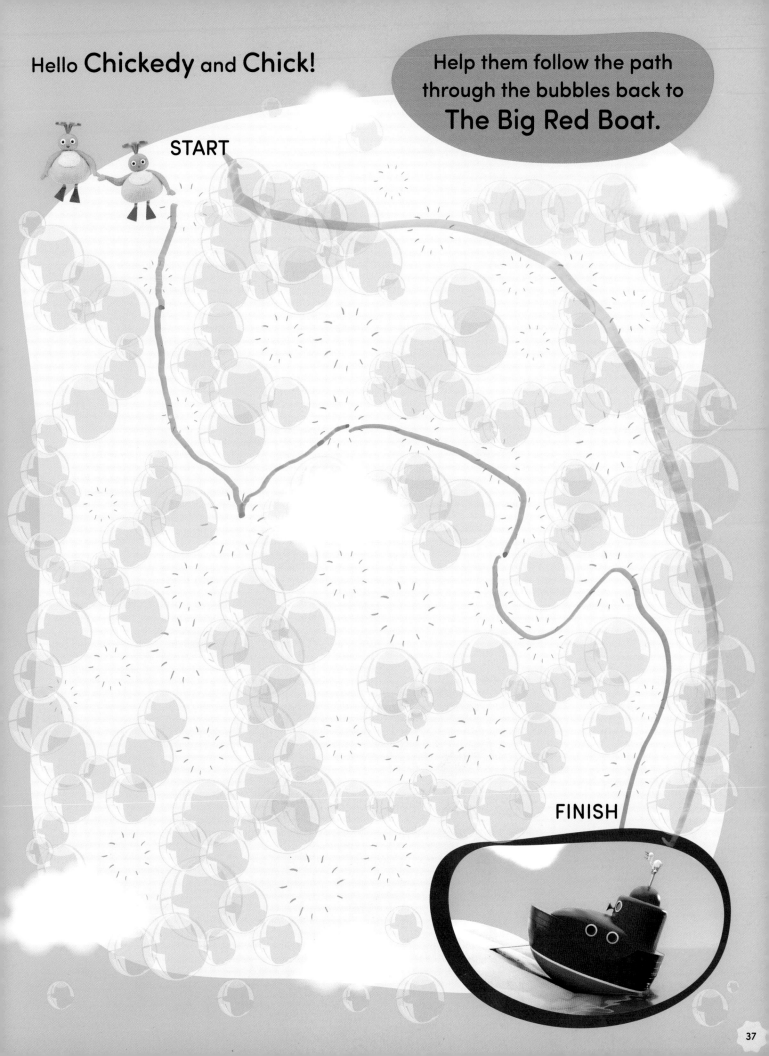

Hello **Chickedy** and **Chick!**

Help them follow the path through the bubbles back to **The Big Red Boat.**

START

FINISH

POP bubbles with the Twirlywoos!

A grown-up will need to help you, and you will need these things:

- Washing-up liquid
- A shallow dish or plate
- Some water
- A ring to blow bubbles through!

What can you use?

Mix the washing-up liquid with water and pour onto the plate. Dip your bubble-blower ring in the liquid, and blow gently through it... Lots of bubbles! How many can you make?

Can you wave your bubble blower through the air, to make even more bubbles?

Now **POP** them all!

Today the **Twirlywoos** are learning something new. All about...
Underneath!

Here is **Peekaboo.** He is UNDERNEATH the rainbow.

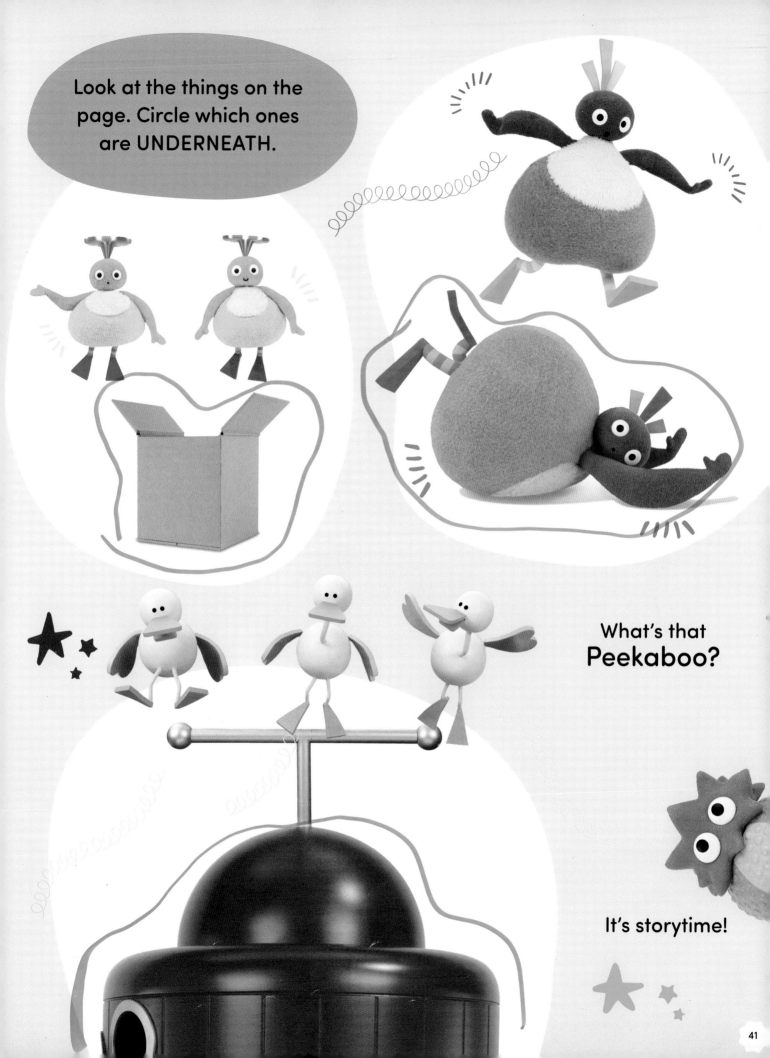

Look at the things on the page. Circle which ones are UNDERNEATH.

What's that Peekaboo?

It's storytime!

Underneath!

Hello **Twirlywoos!**

**Bang!
Bang!**

It's somebody
at the door!

Who is it?

It's The Box!

There's something **UNDERNEATH**
The Box. What could it be?

Look! Colours!

The colours float out of The Box and up into the air.

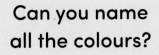

Can you name all the colours?

Peekaboo is floating on the colours.

The colours have disappeared! Where have they gone?

It's a **rainbow!**

Ooh! The **Twirlywoos** like rainbows. **Chickedy** and **Chick** go UNDERNEATH the rainbow. They do a little dance.

Toodloo goes UNDERNEATH the rainbow. She does a little dance with **Chickedy** and **Chick**.

Great BigHoo joins in too. Come on **Twirlywoos**, let's all do a little dance together UNDERNEATH the rainbow!

But now it's time for the
Twirlywoos to go!

Peekaboo
will look after the
rainbow... Bye-bye,
Peekaboo!

We'll see you soon,
Twirlywoos!

Where are the Twirlywoos?
They are all hiding
UNDERNEATH something.

Can you find them?

The **Twirlywoos** are playing hide and seek!

You can play too. What can you hide **UNDERNEATH?**

Draw your best hiding place here

Who can play with you in your house? Can they hide **UNDERNEATH** with you too?

Draw you both hiding here!

48

Toodloo!

Here's Toodloo – but someone is **UNDERNEATH** her!

Join the dots to see who it is.

Chick!

Chickedy!

49

Today the **Twirlywoos** are learning something new. All about... **Behind!**

Look at Great BigHoo.
He is BEHIND Toodloo!

And here's Peekaboo.
He is BEHIND Chickedy and Chick!

Look at the pictures on the page. Can you point out what is BEHIND, and what is in front?

Behind!

Hello,
Peekaboo!

What is
Peekaboo
making?

It's the
**Twirlywoo
Screen!**

What can
you see on the
Twirlywoo Screen?

There's a wall on the Twirlywoo Screen, and there's something BEHIND it.

It's a hand!
The hand waves.
Wave back,
Twirlywoos!

There's another
hand! Wave,
Twirlywoos!

And here are feet
too! And more
hands!

What could
be BEHIND
the wall?

Hello, Octopus!

Oh dear. Octopus is leaving already.

Bye-bye Octopus!

The **Twirlywoos** wave bye-bye to the octopus.

Chickedy!

Chick!

What can we do,
Twirlywoos?
Let's go and see!

Toodloo!

Hoo!

Ooh – look!
There are four walls, and they each have something BEHIND them.
What do you think is BEHIND each one?

Beep!
Beep!

Chickedy!

Hoo!

Toodloo

Boo! We see you, Twirlywoos!

Can you play too? Hide your eyes **BEHIND** your hands! Take them away again – and **Boo!** There you are!

Boo!

We see you too, Peekaboo!

Who can **YOU** play with in your house?

Look at the shadows on the wall BEHIND the Twirlywoos!

Can you match the right shadow to the right Twirlywoo? Draw a line between them.

It's the Octopus from **BEHIND** the wall!

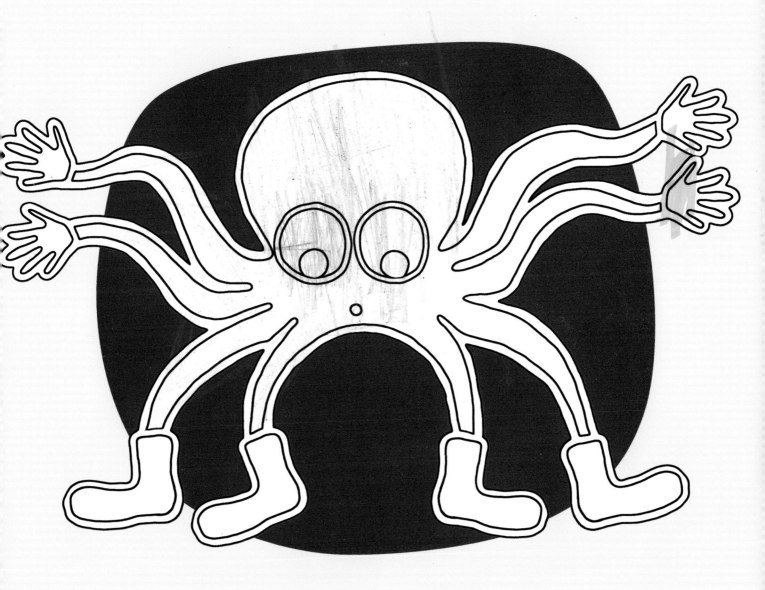

What colour do you want him to be?
Colour him in!

The **Twirlywoos** have been busy! Today we learned all about...

Smaller!

Full! **Pop!**

Underneath!

Behind!

Now it's time to say **bye-bye** to the **Twirlywoos**.

Here come the **Twirly Rings**.

Hoo!

Toodloo!

Chickedy! Chick!

Bye-bye **Twirlywoos!**

And **bye-bye** to you too,
Peekaboo!